LANGUAGE
for
LEARNING

Siegfried Engelmann • Jean Osborn

WORKBOOK
A

 **SRA McGraw-Hill**

Columbus, Ohio

 *A Division of The McGraw·Hill Companies*

SRA/McGraw-Hill

A Division of The McGraw·Hill Companies

Send all inquiries to:
SRA/McGraw-Hill
8787 Orion Place
Columbus, OH 43240-4027

Printed in the United States of America.

ISBN 0-02-674646-8

14 15 POH 06 05

Lesson 1   Name _____

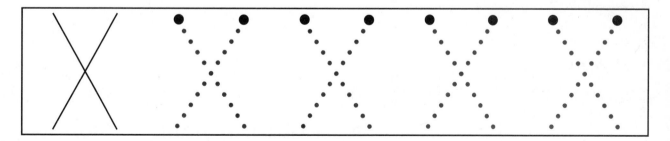

Lesson 2   Name _____

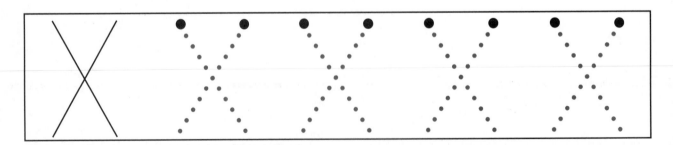

Lesson 3

Name _____

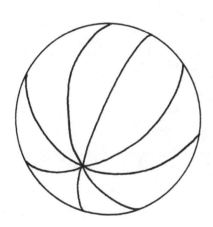

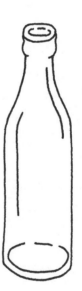

X X X X X X X X X

Lesson 4   Name _____

Lesson 5

Name _____

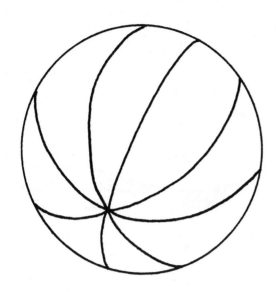

X X X X X

Lesson 6   Name _____

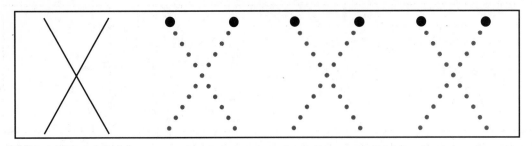 

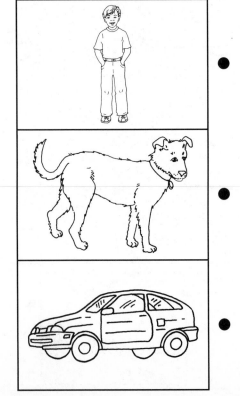

Lesson 7   Name _____

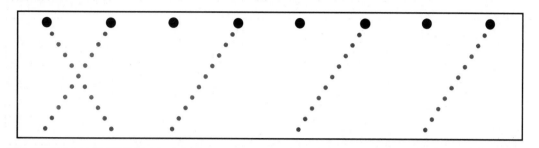

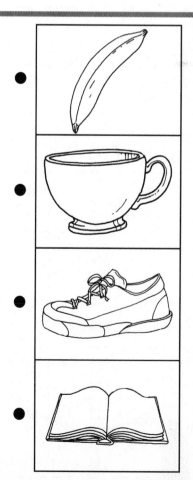

Lesson 8   Name _____

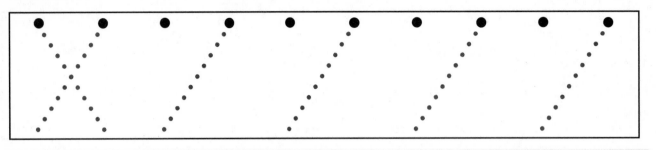

  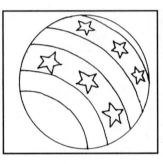 

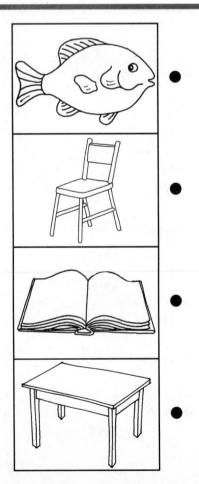 

Lesson 9   Name _____

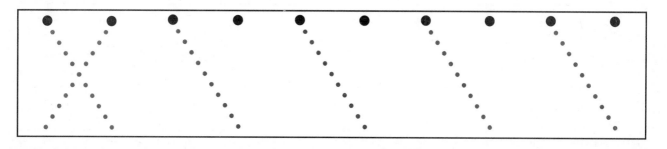

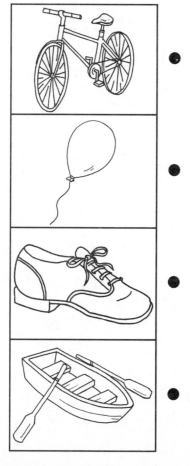 

Lesson 10

Name _____

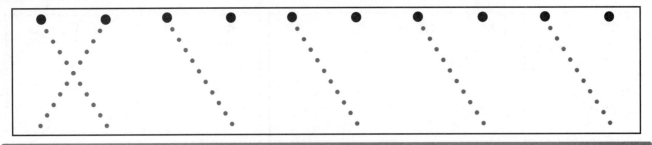

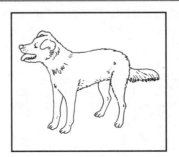

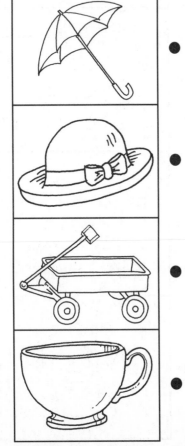
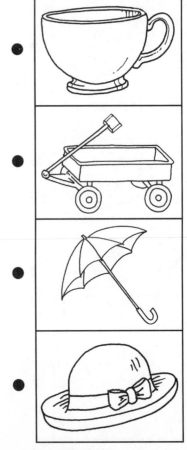

Lesson 11

Name _____

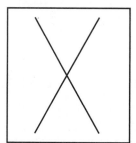 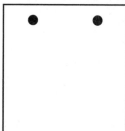 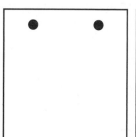  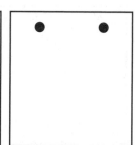

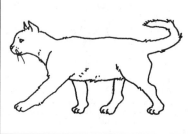

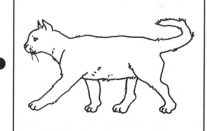

Lesson 12

Name _____

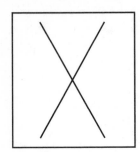  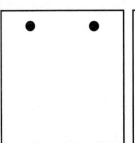 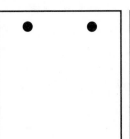 

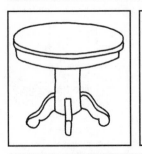    

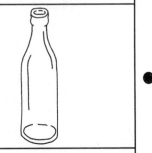

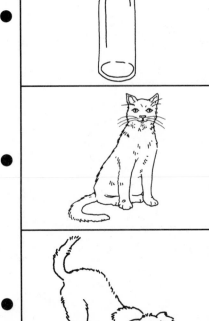

Lesson 13   Name _____

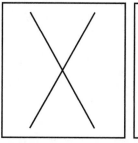 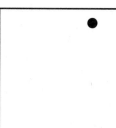 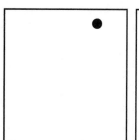 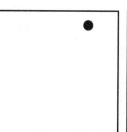 

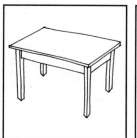    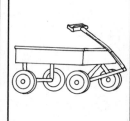

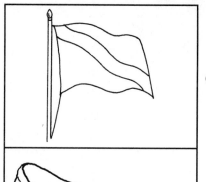 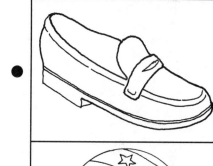

 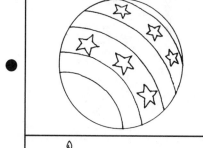

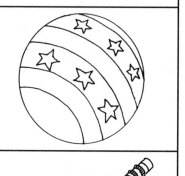 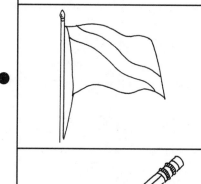

Lesson 14

Name _____

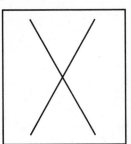 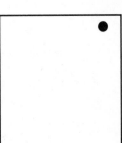 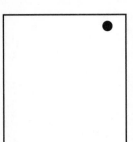  

 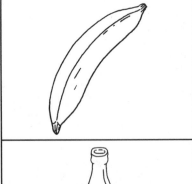

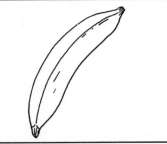 

Lesson 15   Name _____

Lesson 16

Name _____

  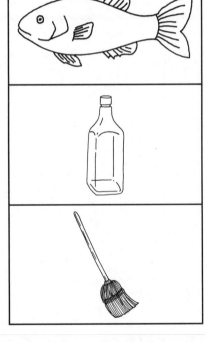

Lesson 17   Name _____

 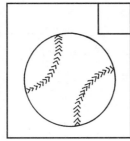 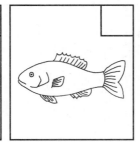  

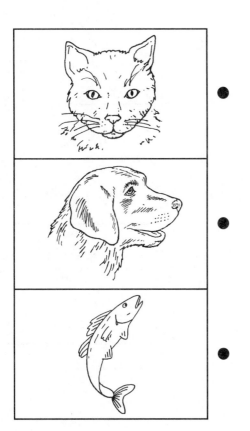 

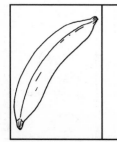

Lesson 19   Name _____

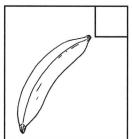   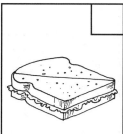 

   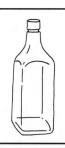   

Lesson 20

Name _____

  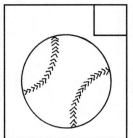  

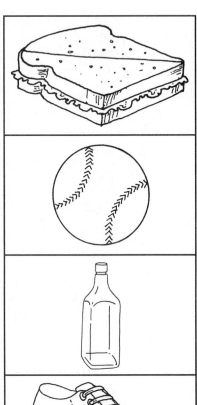

Lesson 21

Name _____

Lesson 22

Name _____

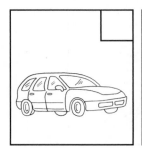 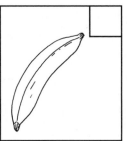  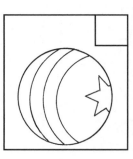 

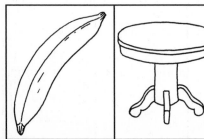 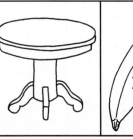    

Lesson 23   Name _____

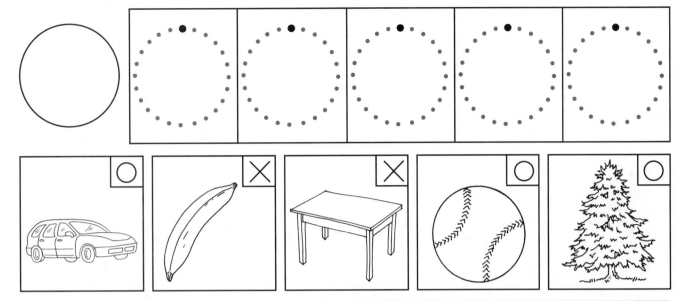

Lesson 24

Name _____

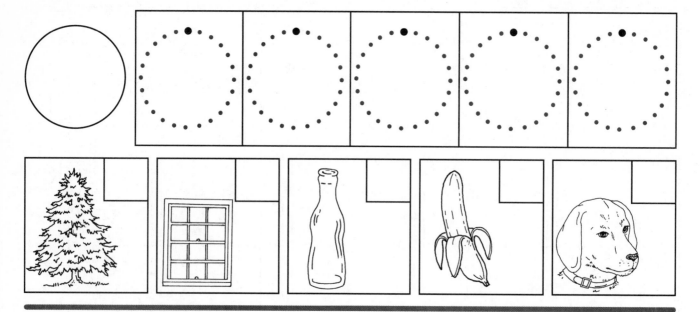

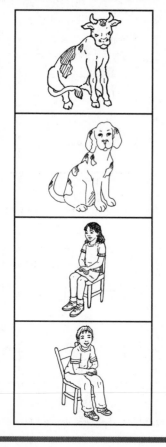
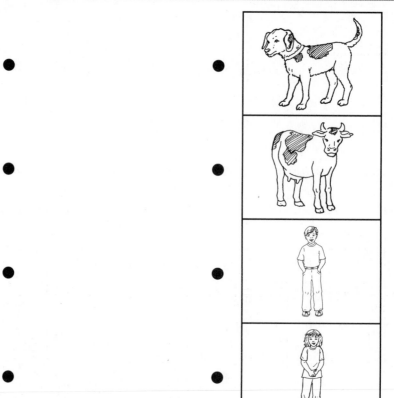

Lesson 25

Name _____

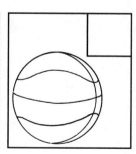

Lesson 26

Name _____

  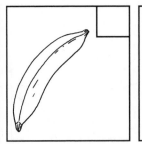 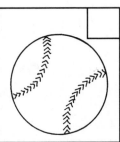 

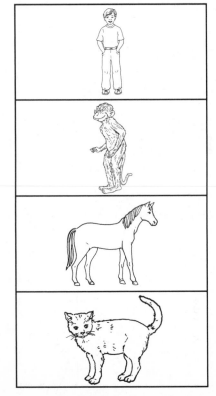

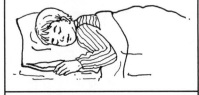

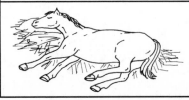

Lesson 27   Name _____

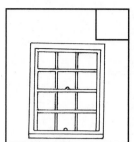  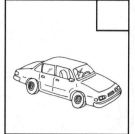  

 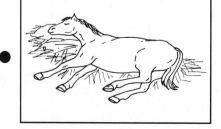  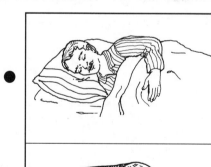

Lesson 28   Name _____

Lesson 29

Name _____

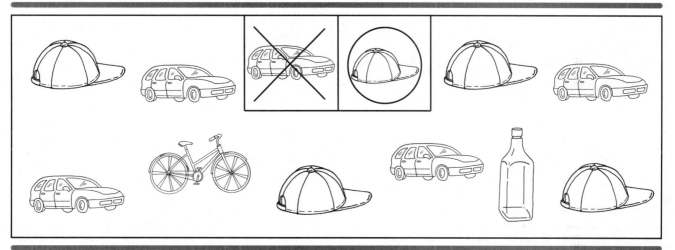

Lesson 30

Name _____

 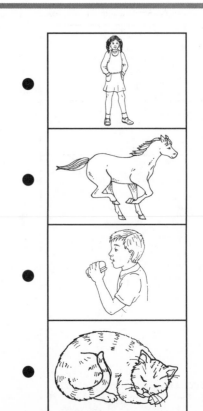

Lesson 31   Name _____

Lesson 33

Name _____

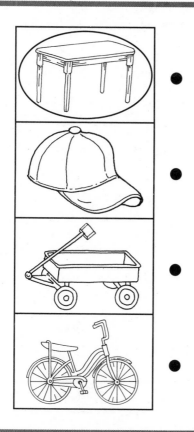 ● ● ● ●   ● ● ● ●

Lesson 34

Name _____

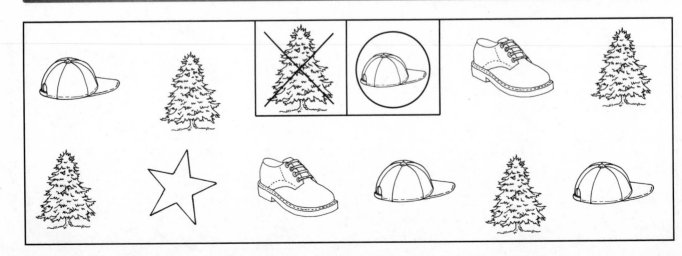

Lesson 35

Name _____

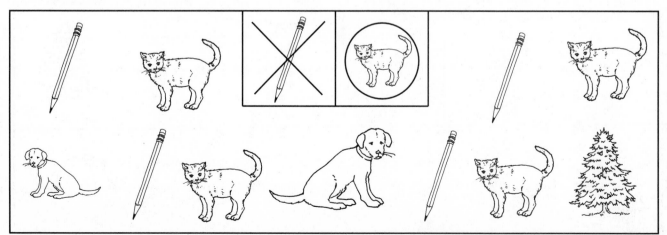

Lesson 36

Name _____

 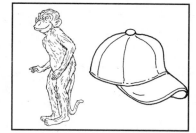 

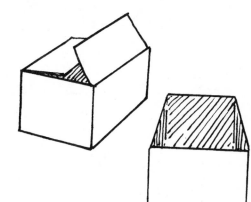

 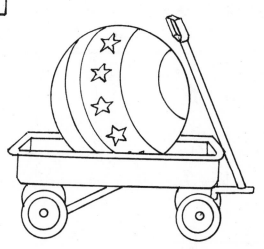

Lesson 36   Name _____

Side 2 _____

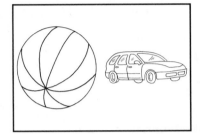

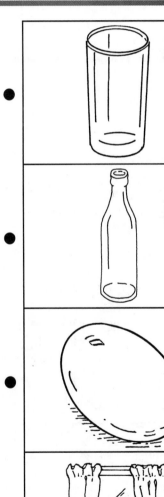

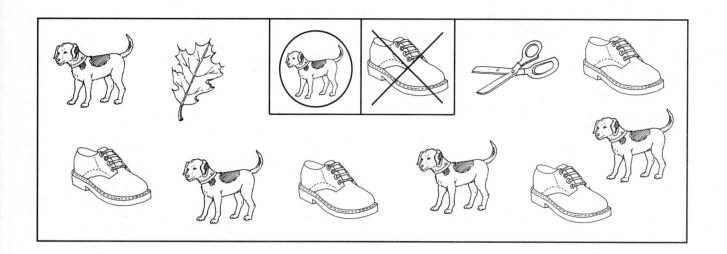

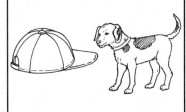

Lesson 38

Name _____

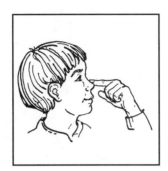 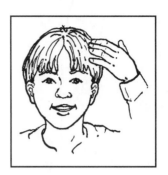

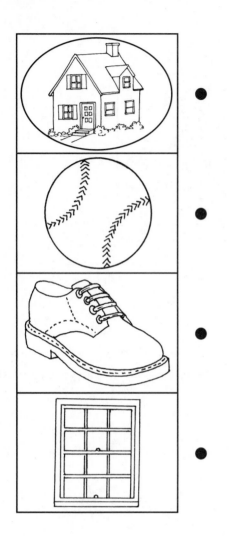

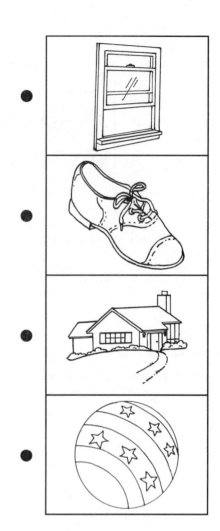

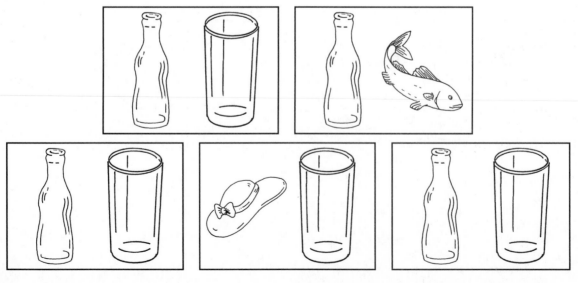

Lesson 40

Name _____

Lesson 40   Name _____

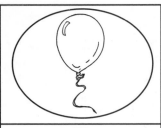
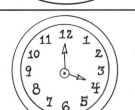

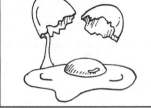

Side 2 _____

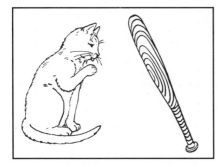
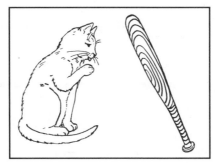

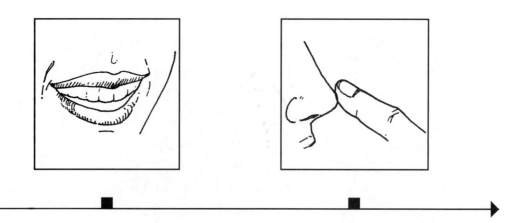

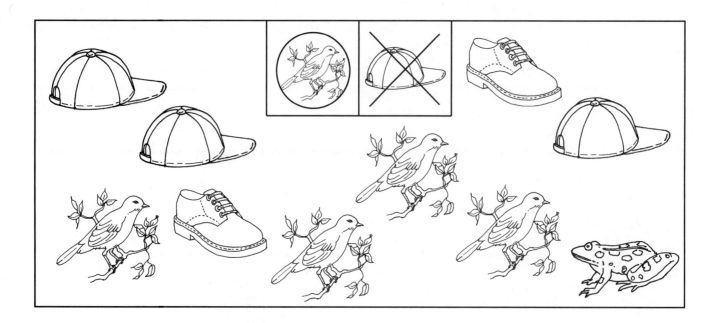

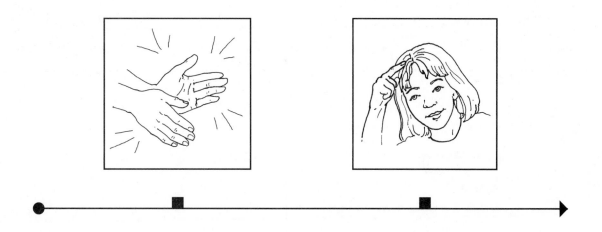

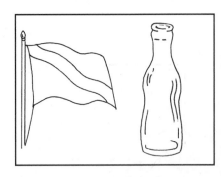 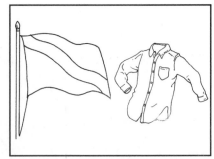

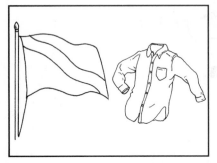 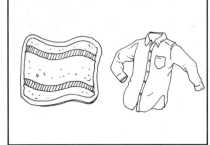 

Name _____

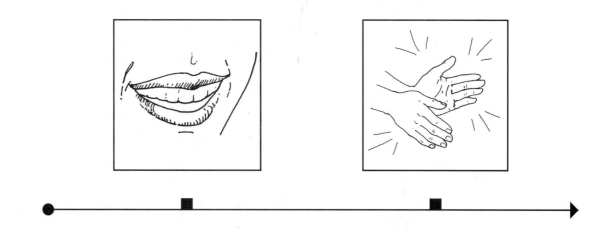

Lesson 43

Name _____

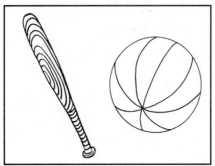 

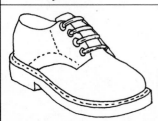 

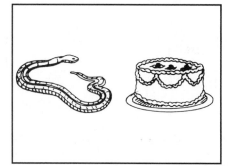

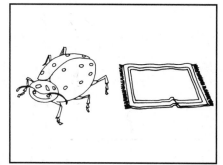

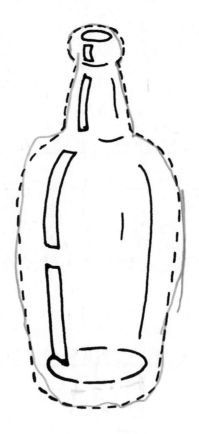

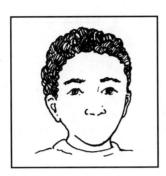 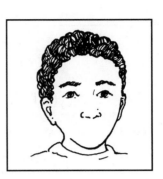

Lesson 45

Name _____

Lesson 46

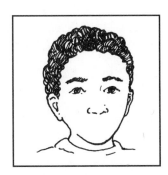 

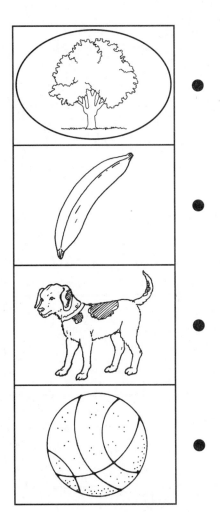 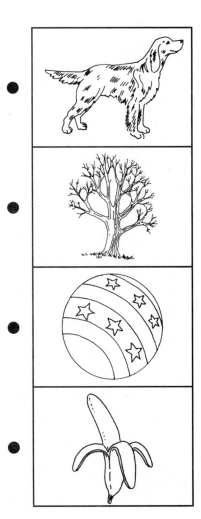

Side 1 _____

Lesson 46

Name _____

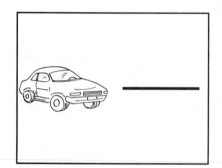 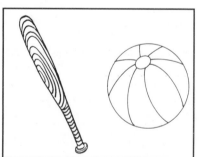 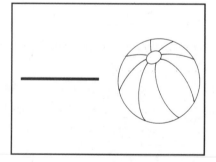

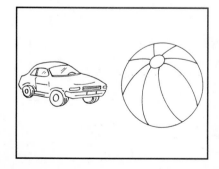  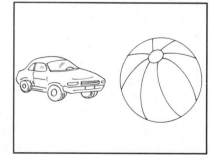

Side 2 _____

Name _____

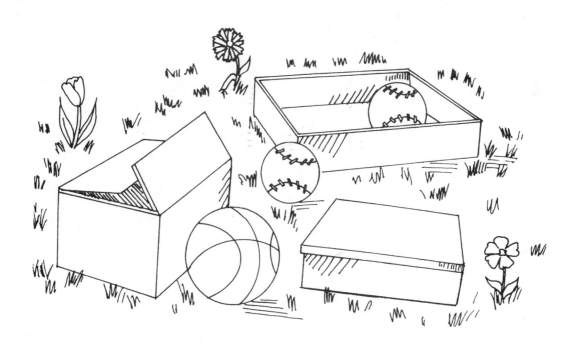

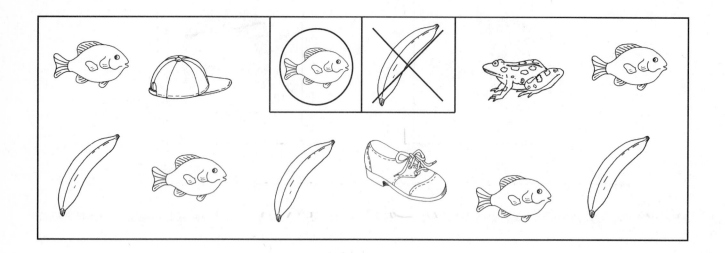

Lesson 48

Name _____

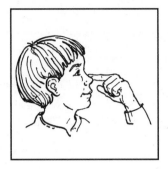 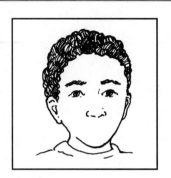

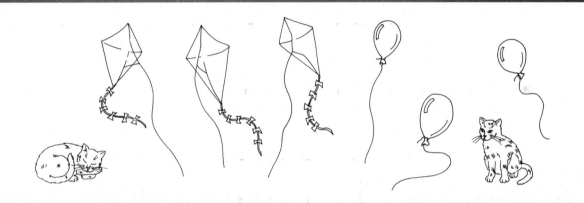

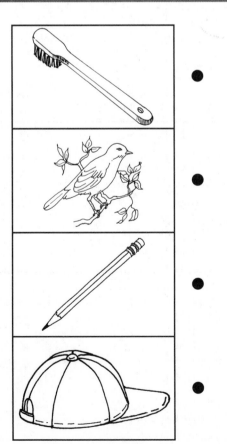 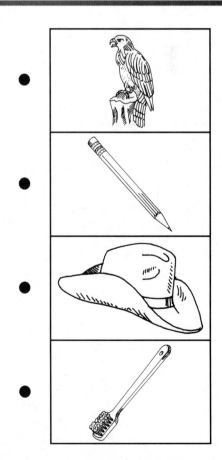

Lesson 48

Name _____

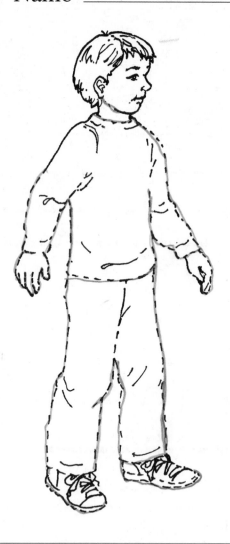

  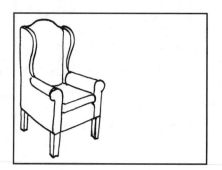

Side 2 _____

X

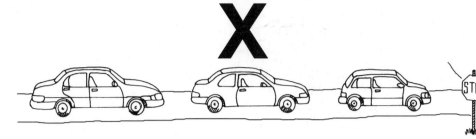

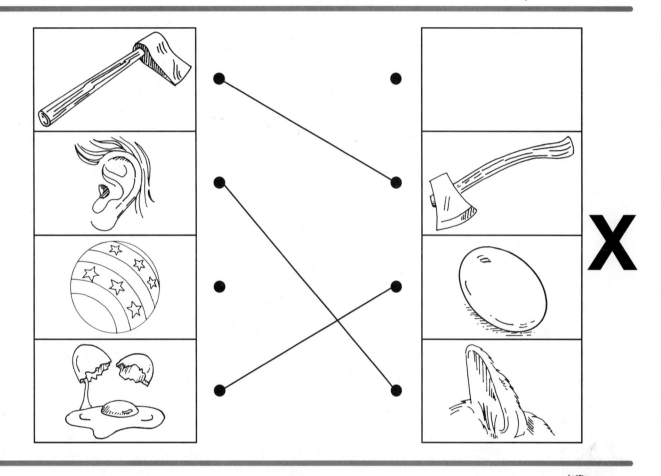

X

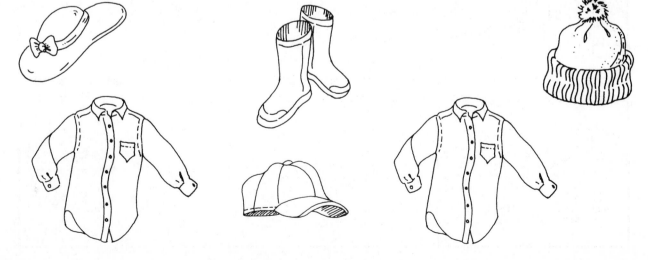

Lesson 49

Name _____

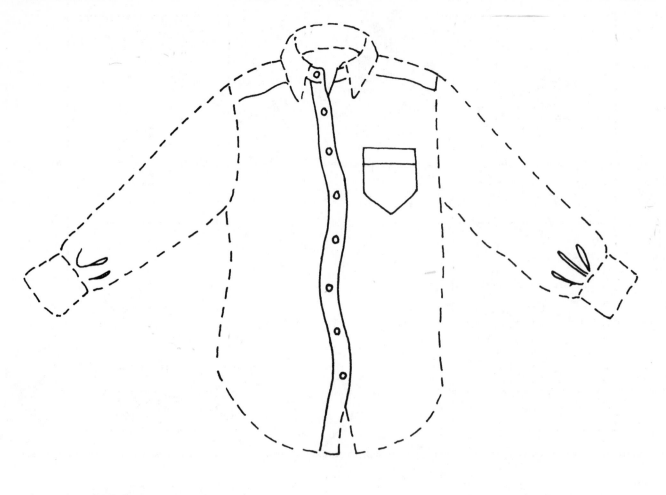

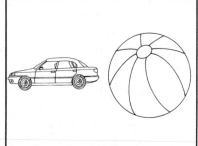
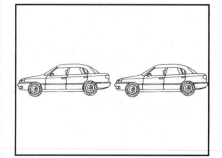

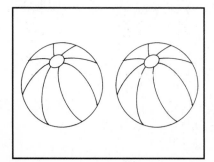
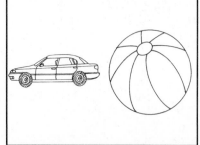
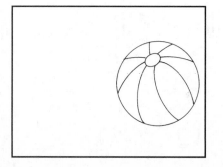

Side 2 _____

Lesson 50

Name _____

Lesson 50   Name _____

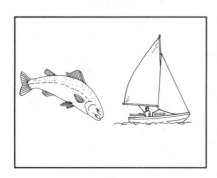  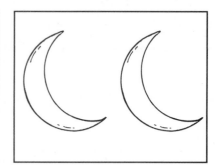

Side 2 _____